Inspiration from the

SAINTS

A Coloring Book
for Prayer and Meditation

Written and illustrated by
Cindi Duft

Pauline
BOOKS & MEDIA
Boston

ISBN 0-8198-3746-6

ISBN 978-0-8198-3746-2

Cover art and design by Cindi Duft

Published by Pauline Books & Media, 50 Saint Pauls Avenue, Boston, MA 02130-3491

Printed in the U.S.A.

www.pauline.org

Pauline Books & Media is the publishing house of the Daughters of St. Paul, an international congregation of women religious serving the Church with the communications media.

1 2 3 4 5 6 7 8 9   23 22 21 20 19

To Linda,
whose encouragement
made this work possible.

CONTENTS

Come now,
flee for a while
from your occupations,
escape for a moment
from the tumult
of your thoughts.
Cast aside your
burdensome cares,
put away all
distractions;
free yourself for
a while for God and
rest a little while in him.

—St. Anselm

Introduction

Catholicism and the history of art have a long and complementary relationship. Like prayer, the beauty of art can lift our hearts and minds to understand God. Combining art and prayer is a truly powerful way to connect with God who is Beauty itself.

This coloring book is an introduction to praying with religious art with the help of the saints. Alive with God in heaven, the saints are part of our spiritual family. They are always ready to pray for us or to offer any other help that God empowers them to give. The saints' lives are like beautiful works of art for God that help us learn how to live the Gospel. Their examples and inspired writings can help us to deepen our relationship with God on our own paths to holiness. Beautiful works of art for God, the saints' lives help us learn how to live the Gospel.

St. John Paul II wrote in his *Letter to Artists* that beauty is a call to transcendence and a key to the mystery of God. In other words, beauty communicates truth. I hope that this book will spark an interest in you to meditate more on Catholic art and to pray with and learn more about the saints.

Let's make something beautiful!

Inner Peace and St. Augustine

Augustine (354-430) was born in northern Africa to a strong Christian mother and a successful, pagan father. He was a very intelligent boy who grew up to study rhetoric and philosophy. Distracted by worldly desires for achievement and pleasure, Augustine lived a sinful life for many years. But his mother, St. Monica, prayed for him endlessly.

One day, Augustine met St. Ambrose, the bishop of Milan. With Ambrose's help, Augustine began to see Christianity with new eyes. Finally, Augustine had a moment of conversion when he read a passage from St. Paul's Letter to the Romans. He went on to be ordained a priest and became bishop of Hippo. Augustine is now revered as one of the greatest theologians in the Church. His autobiography, *The Confessions*, is a classic still read all over the world.

This illustration is inspired by a kaleidoscope. The pieces inside a kaleidoscope tumble and fall as a person turns it. The patterns are controlled by the person turning the kaleidoscope and can be attractive or unattractive. In Augustine's early life, the influence of the world encouraged him to put success and pleasure above all else. Like the pieces in a kaleidoscope, he was tumbling and falling. But when he committed himself to Christ, his heart was transformed and finally made whole. With God in control, Augustine's life shone with the light of Christ. As he sought the Holy Spirit to enlighten his conscience, the world's power over him subsided. He could now dwell in the security of Christ's love and truth. With Christ as his center and rock, Augustine found true peace.

As you color, consider the distractions that cause you to fall and tumble away from God. What or who do you feel controls your life? How might things be different if you gave more control to God?

"You move us to delight in praising you; for you have formed us for yourself, and our hearts are restless until they find rest in you."

— St. Augustine, *The Confessions*

THIS VERY MOMENT I MAY,
♡ IF I DESIRE, BECOME ♡
A FRIEND OF GOD.

—ST. AUGUSTINE

Self-Discovery and St. Thomas

When the Apostle Thomas (1st century) heard that Jesus had appeared to the other disciples after the resurrection, he declared, "Unless I see the mark of the nails in his hands, and put my finger in the mark of the nails and my hand in his side, I will not believe" (Jn 20:25). For this reason, Thomas is often referred to as "the doubter." But as Fr. Otto Hophan, OFM, once theorized in *The Apostles*, Thomas' doubt about the risen Christ might have been due to melancholy rather than a lack of faith. For where else would Thomas have been while the others were hiding in fear? Out amidst the danger!

Perhaps Thomas was simply devastated that Jesus made his first appearance to the Apostles while he was absent. Of course, it is impossible for us to know Thomas' mind. But our actions, thoughts, and feelings cannot always be taken at face value. Deeper beliefs, fears, and ideas are often at play. What lies beneath our doubt might actually be pride, laziness, fear of disappointment, or the belief that we cannot be loved or forgiven. Self-discovery can be a difficult, but also helpful, journey as it helps us to know both ourselves and God better.

This illustration is drawn from a traditional Greek Orthodox Byzantine icon. Icons are not realistic portrayals of three-dimensional objects. Rather, they are two-dimensional images that portray deep realities with rich symbolism. In this icon, Thomas, often depicted as a beardless youth, climbs a mountain that resembles a staircase—a symbol of spiritual ascent. The presence of vegetation signifies life. The scroll, often held by apostles and prophets, symbolizes holy wisdom. Thomas' gaze is fixed on God's hand of blessing and his hands are outstretched, indicating that he is offering his life's work to God while also asking for continued help and guidance.

As you color, ask the Holy Spirit to reveal what fears or false beliefs might lie beneath any doubts you experience.

"Test us, O Lord, you who know all truth, that we may know ourselves."

— St. Teresa of Ávila, *Interior Castle*

ST. THOMAS

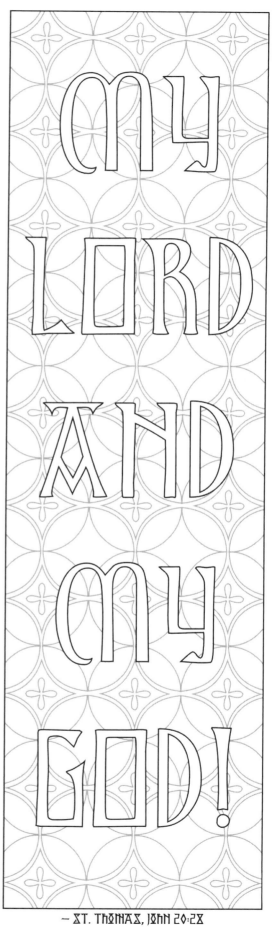

MY LORD AND MY GOD!

— ST. THOMAS, JOHN 20:28

Trust and Bl. Julian of Norwich

Julian of Norwich (c. 1342-c. 1423) lived during a time of great suffering amidst poverty, famine, and the Black Death. When she was thirty, she came down with the plague. She only narrowly escaped death after one day receiving a mystical vision of Christ bleeding on the Cross. That day she had fifteen more visions. Julian later withdrew from the world to live as a recluse, devoting her life completely to God. She spent the rest of her life praying, meditating upon her visions, writing, and giving spiritual counsel to visitors.

Never officially beatified, Julian of Norwich is nevertheless honored in the Church for her great holiness and time-honored meditations on the love of God. Her writings are full of hope, understanding, and encouragement. In coming to know the heart of God, she wrote, "I saw no manner of wrath in God, neither for a short time nor for long." Trust was also a theme in her writings: "If anywhere on earth a lover of God is always kept safe from falling, I know nothing of it, for it was not shown to me. But this was shown: that in falling and in rising we are ever preciously kept in one love." Notably, her writings are the earliest surviving English texts authored by a woman.

This illustration is drawn from an intricate medieval design. During Julian's lifetime, advances in engineering enabled the construction of buildings with great scale and complexity, which gave rise to great Gothic cathedrals. Art and architecture became more intricate and ornate to reflect the beauty and glory of God. Noticeable use of geometry and mathematics in medieval designs such as this reflect the order, logic, and genius with which God creates. Accompanying this design is Jesus' response to Julian when she wondered why God allowed Adam and Eve to sin. In the midst of her anxiety, Jesus reassured Julian of his ultimate victory saying, "All shall be well and all shall be well and all manner of things shall be well."

As you color, ask to be shown God's love for you so that you can always put your trust in him.

"For I am convinced that neither death, nor life, nor angels, nor rulers, nor things present, nor things to come, nor powers, nor height, nor depth, nor anything else in all creation, will be able to separate us from the love of God in Christ Jesus our Lord."

— St. Paul, Romans 8:38-39

all shall be well and all shall be well

and all manner of things shall be well

—Bl. Julian of Norwich

Patience and St. Francis de Sales

Francis de Sales (1567–1622) was born to a wealthy French family. He studied law and theology under the Jesuits. Despite pressure from his family to pursue a career that was more lucrative and esteemed, Francis chose to become a priest. After his ordination, he was sent to Geneva where he reached out to the many Calvinists in the area. Through his sense of humor, gentleness, wisdom, and humility, Francis brought many people back to the Catholic faith. He was a teacher, writer, bishop, administrator, and one of the great leaders of the Counter-Reformation. Yet for all of his accomplishments, Francis was and still is very approachable.

The patron saint of writers, Francis wrote many books and pamphlets to help the faithful. His *Introduction to the Devout Life* assured Christians that holiness is possible for everyone, even in the midst of life's busyness and stress. Francis' writing provides balanced, helpful, and encouraging advice for people in any state of life who seek union with God. For people who lose patience with themselves, he wrote, "We would always like to have a little consolation, a little sugar in our tea, that is to say, the feeling of love and tenderness, and as a result consolation. And, in like manner, we so wish to be without imperfections. But we must have patience to belong to human nature, and not to angelic nature. Our imperfections should not please us . . . but they should also not astonish us, or take away our courage."

The illustration is based on an 11th-century stone carving at St-André-de-Sorède Abbey in Roussillon, France. Though the figure is of one of the evangelists, his almost comical expression communicates Francis' down-to-earth nature and the importance he placed on not taking oneself too seriously.

As you color, ask yourself, "How patient am I with my imperfections?" Ask God to help you to grow in holiness and patience.

"Do not worry about anything, but in everything by prayer and supplication with thanksgiving let your requests be made known to God. And the peace of God, which surpasses all understanding, will guard your hearts and your minds in Christ Jesus."

— St. Paul, Philippians 4:6–7

BE PATIENT WITH
EVERYONE, BUT ABOVE
ALL WITH YOURSELF.

— ST. FRANCIS DE SALES

Forgiveness and St. Elizabeth of Hungary

Elizabeth (1207–1231) was born the third child of loving parents, King Andrew II and Queen Gertrude. She was fortunate to be born a princess but, from a very young age, Elizabeth also suffered much heartache. When she was only four, her parents arranged her marriage and sent her to be raised in the German royal court. Within two years, Elizabeth's mother was murdered by Hungarian nobles. Thankfully, her betrothed, Ludwig, was a good friend to Elizabeth. The two came to love each other very much and married when Elizabeth was fourteen. The loving couple had four children, and Ludwig always admired and supported Elizabeth's faith and acts of charity.

Elizabeth was known for her compassion for the poor and needy. She had a public hospital built and regularly distributed food to the hungry. However, some of Ludwig's family members were not happy with Elizabeth's great generosity. After Ludwig died of the plague on his way to fight in the Crusades, Ludwig's brother made clear that Elizabeth and her children were not welcome in the castle. Elizabeth found her children a safe home and went to live in poverty with the Franciscans. There, she joyfully served the poor, sick, and elderly for the rest of her life—a short three years.

The illustration depicts a wheel wrapped with wheat and roses that represent a well-known miracle associated with Elizabeth. According to legend, she was once bringing bread to the poor and was surprised by a family member who demanded that she reveal what was in her cloak. When Elizabeth opened her cloak, roses fell out. The wheel is meant to represent her willingness to keep moving forward, day after day, in her good works.

As you color, consider the difficulties that Elizabeth faced in life. Reflect on how she did not allow resentment, bitterness, defensiveness, loss, or anger to keep her from living a holy life of service.

"As in heaven your will is punctually performed, so may it be done on earth by all creatures, particularly in me and by me."

— St. Elizabeth of Hungary

See that none of you repays evil for evil ...
Rejoice always, pray without ceasing,
give thanks in all circumstances.

—1 Thessalonians 5:15-18

Confidence and St. Jude

Jude (1st century) was one of the twelve Apostles and most likely a relative of Jesus. He is known as the patron saint of hopeless or impossible causes. Perhaps Jude was inspired when he heard the Blessed Mother retell the story of the Annunciation when the Angel Gabriel assured her, "Nothing will be impossible with God" (Lk 1:37). Jesus worked many miracles when Jude was present, including curing the ill and the blind, casting out demons, raising people from the dead, and calming storms. After all that Jude witnessed, especially the resurrection of Jesus, he must have truly been confident that *nothing* is impossible for God.

Today, some people argue that God is either distant or dead. But nothing could be further from the truth. God is just as active now as he was in Jude's time. God truly exists and his everlasting love cannot be limited or erased by people's disbelief. Evidence of God's action in our modern world can be seen by anyone who genuinely seeks to discover it. Jude is a good saint to ask to intercede for family members or friends who experience serious difficulty or doubt in God's love or existence.

The illustration is drawn from Rembrandt's painting "Christ in the Storm on the Lake of Galilee." In the Gospel of Mark, Jesus rebukes and calms the storm and then asks the disciples, "Why are you afraid? Have you still no faith?" (4:40). In life, when the storms of doubt and fear assail us, we can remember that God is all-powerful and can work miracles, even when all seems hopeless.

As you color, ask God to renew your hope as you consider the difficult situations in your life or in the lives of loved ones.

"*Christ commands the storm, and everything is calm (see Mt 8:23–27). . . . Do not let the waves overcome you when your heart is troubled. Yet as we are only human, if the wind stirs up our souls, let us not despair. Let us instead awake Christ so we can sail on a tranquil sea, and arrive at our country.*"

— St. Augustine of Hippo, Sermon 13

Love and Our Blessed Mother

Mary played a key role in our salvation when she consented to be the mother of Jesus, the Son of God (see Lk 1:26–38). Among all the saints, Mary's holiness shines most brilliantly. The mother of the King, or the queen mother, Mary takes on the traditional role of advocating for the people. We can ask Mary to intercede for our needs just as she interceded for the couple at the wedding at Cana (see Jn 2:1–12). Today, God has given Mary another important mission as the Mother of the Church who helps all of her children to have a deeper relationship with her Son.

Over the centuries, Mary's important role in the Church is demonstrated in countless apparitions, miracles, healings, and victories. Like any good mother, when Mary appears in various places all over the world, she gives both stern admonitions and gentle promises of love. In 1531, Mary appeared to St. Juan Diego in Mexico and said, "I am the compassionate mother of you and of all the people here in this land, and of the other various peoples who love me, who cry out to me, who seek me, who trust me. Here I will listen to their weeping and their sorrows in order to remedy and heal all their various afflictions, miseries, and torments."

The illustration depicts the Miraculous Medal that Mary instructed St. Catherine Labouré to make when she appeared to her in Rue du Bac, Paris, France in 1830. Around the medal are the national flowers of countries where Mary has reportedly appeared and where there is great Marian devotion. Starting at the base and rotating clockwise are: the dahlia of Mexico, *Erythrina crista-galli* of Argentina, chamomile of Russia, golden lilies of Bosnia and Herzegovina, lavender of Portugal, shamrocks of Ireland, sunflowers of the Ukraine, lotus of Vietnam and Egypt, pyrethrum of Rwanda, poppies of Poland and Belgium, irises of France, sampaguita of the Philippines, and orchids of Venezuela.

As you color, consider how well you know the Blessed Mother. Ask Mary to lead you to an ever-deeper love for her Son, Jesus Christ.

We fly to your protection,
O holy Mother of God.
Hear our petitions
in our necessities,
and deliver us from all dangers,
O glorious and blessed Virgin.

— Oldest known prayer to the Virgin Mary,
found in a Greek papyrus c. 300

Dependability and St. Joseph

Joseph, a descendant of King David, was a righteous and humble man who trustingly accepted great responsibility from God. When an angel appeared in a dream and told Joseph to take Mary as his wife, even though she was pregnant before their marriage, he accepted and believed (see Mt 1:20-21). Joseph also protected the infant Jesus from a jealous king who was willing to kill every baby boy in the vicinity to ensure his death (see Mt 2:16).

God entrusted Joseph with an immense duty, and Joseph showed himself to be dependable. Joseph provided for his family, honored and loved Mary, and raised the Son of God with great devotion and attention. His life exemplified the qualities of holy fatherhood: loyalty, protection, intelligence, capability, goodness, provision, and love. In today's world, many have low expectations of fathers. And, unfortunately, the importance of good fathers is often downplayed. But we can turn to Joseph as a model and inspiration for all men, especially those who take on the role of fatherhood in any way.

The illustration is drawn from a section of a wooden altar from St. Nicholas Church in Kalkar, Germany. The "Altar of the Seven Sorrows" was intricately carved in the 16th century by sculptor Henrik Douverman. Jesse, the father of King David, sleeps at the base of the altar, and an elaborate tree grows from him. The tree encircles 150 other figures from Jesus' lineage and salvation history. Jesse's attendant points to a scroll, perhaps one that prophesies the coming of Christ: "A shoot shall come out from the stump of Jesse, and a branch shall grow out of his roots" (Is 11:1).

As you color, pray for any men you know who need encouragement to live in holiness.

"Do not let loyalty and faithfulness forsake you; bind them around your neck, write them on the tablet of your heart."

— Proverbs 3:3

Courage and St. Patrick

When Patrick (c. 387–c. 461) was a teenager, he was kidnapped from his homeland of Roman Britain by pirates and forced into slavery in Ireland. Not very pious at the time, Patrick turned to God in captivity and became a very devoted Christian. He worked as a shepherd, and this gave him time to pray and grow close to God. After about six years, Patrick courageously escaped his captors and returned home.

Patrick soon felt called by God to return to Ireland as a missionary to convert the hearts of the people. He was ordained a priest, then consecrated bishop and sent to Ireland in 432. He spent the rest of his life educating the Irish people and forming them in the spiritual life. Patrick's ministry was fraught with danger and persecution as he tried to evangelize the tribes of Ireland. But he also found that many people yearned to live for Christ. He built churches and monasteries, organized dioceses, and created the infrastructure of the Church in Ireland.

· This illustration is borrowed from the *Book of Kells*, a gorgeous illuminated manuscript of the four Gospels. The book has been attributed to Columban monks from monasteries in Iona, Scotland, and Kells, Ireland—monasteries that may have never existed had it not been for the courageous work of St. Patrick. The illustration includes symbols of the evangelists: angel (Matthew), eagle (John), lion (Mark), and ox (Luke). There are also a variety of Celtic knots, which symbolize eternity, life's interconnectedness, and life in God. One stanza from the hymn "I Bind Unto Myself Today" based on the "Breastplate of St. Patrick" prayer is shown in the illustration. Four more stanzas are printed below. Attributed to St. Patrick, the prayer is a testament to his reliance on God and his desire to cooperate with God's will for his life.

As you color, meditate on the words of Patrick's prayer and his courage in following God's call. In what areas of your life could you use a little more courage?

Against the demon snares of sin,
The vice that gives temptation force,
The natural lusts that war within,
The hostile men that mar my course;
Or few or many, far or nigh,
In every place and in all hours,
Against their fierce hostility,
I bind to me these holy powers.

Against all Satan's spells and wiles,
Against false words of heresy,
Against the knowledge that defiles,
Against the heart's idolatry,

Against the wizard's evil craft,
Against the death wound and the
    burning,
The choking wave, the poisoned
    shaft,
Protect me, Christ, till thy returning.

Christ be with me, Christ within me,
Christ behind me, Christ before me,
Christ beside me, Christ to win me,
Christ to comfort and restore me.
Christ beneath me, Christ above me,
Christ in quiet, Christ in danger,

Christ in hearts of all that love me,
Christ in mouth of friend and
    stranger.

I bind unto myself the Name,
The strong Name of the Trinity;
By invocation of the same.
The Three in One, and One
    in Three,
By Whom all nature hath creation,
Eternal Father, Spirit, Word:
Praise to the Lord of my salvation,
Salvation is of Christ the Lord.

I bind unto myself today the power of God to hold and lead,

his eye to watch, his might to stay, his ear to hearken to my need,

the wisdom of my God to teach, his hand to guide, his shield to ward,

the word of God to give me speech, his heavenly host to be my guard.

Listening and St. Francis of Assisi

When Francis (c. 1181–1226) was young, he loved to go to parties and to wear fancy clothes. As he began his career as a soldier, he dreamed of attaining great glory. He was caught in a whirlwind of worldly pleasures and dreams and nothing else was important to him. But then after fighting in a battle between Assisi and Perugia, he was captured and held for ransom. In prison, Francis began to experience a conversion. Eventually, he gave up his life of wealth and security and found joy in embracing poverty and obedience.

One day Francis was praying in the small, abandoned chapel of San Damiano when he heard a voice from the crucifix telling him, "Rebuild my church." Francis understood God's command to mean that he should set to work on renovating the small chapel. Little did he know then but his love, simplicity, holiness, and preaching would begin a renewal that far exceeded little San Damiano. Many men and women, inspired by his life of holiness, began to follow Francis. He received permission to begin a religious order after Pope Innocent III had a dream of Francis holding up a church, symbolizing the revitalization that Francis would bring to the Church.

The illustration depicts the San Damiano crucifix that Francis prayed before when he heard the voice of God. Jesus is bleeding, but his posture and expression are that of an embrace. His outstretched arms invite us into the story and into his family. The crucifix contains scenes from the crucifixion, the resurrection, and the ascension. At the top of the cross, angels welcome the ascended Christ into heaven, and the hand of the Father blesses him. The larger figures near Christ's waist are the Blessed Mother, St. John, St. Mary Magdalene, Mary of Clopas, and likely the centurion who asked Jesus to cure his son (see Mt 8:5–13). Francis often prayed the words that are around the cross.

As you color, try to embrace the same joy and peace that Francis often felt and listen to what Jesus has to say to you.

"Almighty, most holy, most high, and supreme God, highest good, all good, wholly good, who alone are good. To you we render all praise, all glory, all thanks, all honor, all blessing, and we shall always refer all good to you. Amen."

— St. Francis of Assisi, conclusion of "The Praises"

Most High, glorious God, bring light to the darkness of my heart. Give me right faith,

certain hope & perfect charity, insight & wisdom, so I can always observe Thy holy and true command.

IHSNAZARE REXIVDEORV

— ST. FRANCIS OF ASSISI

True Joy and St. John the Baptist

Since the first covenant with Abraham over 4,000 years ago, God began paving the way for the coming of his Son who would reconcile humanity to himself. John the Baptist (1st century), a relative of Jesus, had the honor of announcing the long-awaited coming of the Messiah. The people acclaimed John as a prophet, and his popularity was great. However, John's only concern was to draw people to Christ. John constantly reminded others that he was simply the forerunner of someone greater.

On one occasion, some of John's disciples were upset that John's followers were leaving him to follow Jesus. John responded, "No one can receive anything except what has been given from heaven. You yourselves are my witnesses that I said, 'I am not the Messiah, but I have been sent ahead of him.' He who has the bride is the bridegroom. The friend of the bridegroom, who stands and hears him, rejoices greatly at the bridegroom's voice. For this reason my joy has been fulfilled. He must increase, but I must decrease" (Jn 3:27–30). Not long after this, John was imprisoned by Herod and beheaded. John accepted his fate in faith, knowing that his mission was complete.

The illustration is reminiscent of the fanfare that surrounded Jesus' triumphal entry into Jerusalem just days before his passion, death, and resurrection. Crowds surrounded Jesus and covered the road before him with palm branches and cloaks (see Mt 21:1–11). They praised Jesus as the Son of David. The people believed that the King of Kings and Lord of Lords had come! John the Baptist had died by this point, but his short life had prepared the way for Jesus the King. The dying flowers symbolize John's brief but fruitful life.

As you color, meditate on John's words "He must increase, but I must decrease" and consider how these words and this attitude brought him joy.

When John the Baptist was born, his father Zechariah
spoke this prophecy:

"Blessed be the Lord God of Israel,
   for he has looked favorably on his people
      and redeemed them.
He has raised up a mighty savior for us
   in the house of his servant David,
as he spoke through the mouth of his holy prophets
      from of old,
   that we would be saved from our enemies and
      from the hand of all who hate us.
Thus he has shown the mercy promised to our
      ancestors,
   and has remembered his holy covenant,
the oath that he swore to our ancestor Abraham,

to grant us that we, being rescued from the hands
      of our enemies,
might serve him without fear, in holiness and
      righteousness before him all our days.
And you, child, will be called the prophet of the
   Most High;
   for you will go before the Lord to prepare his ways,
to give knowledge of salvation to his people
   by the forgiveness of their sins.
By the tender mercy of our God,
   the dawn from on high will break upon us,
to give light to those who sit in darkness and in the
      shadow of death,
   to guide our feet into the way of peace."

— THE CANTICLE OF ZECHARIAH, LUKE 1:68–79

IHS

must increase

must decrease

— st. john the baptist, john 3:30

Leadership and Bl. Anacleto González Flores

Catholicism was violently suppressed by the government of Mexico in the early 20th century. Tensions between the secular government and Catholics broke into war in 1926. President Calles, a virulent atheist, had attempted to enact anti-clerical articles from the Mexican Constitution of 1917. Rather than allow the practice of their faith to be forbidden, many Catholics bravely opposed the government. *¡Viva Cristo Rey!* and *¡Viva la Virgen de Guadalupe!* ("Long live Christ the King!" and "Long live the Virgin of Guadalupe!") were the battle cries of the *Cristeros*, many of whom willingly sacrificed their lives for their faith.

Anacleto González Flores (1888–1927) was active in a Catholic youth organization when tensions were brewing. He taught catechism, and was involved in charitable works. As a young man, he considered the priesthood but discerned that God had a different calling for him. He went to law school, married María Concepción, and the couple had two children. He founded *Union Popular*, an organization that non-violently demonstrated against the persecutions. After four of his friends were murdered, he joined the *National League for the Defense of Religious Freedom* in support of the coming rebellion. However, Anacleto continued to seek non-violent solutions to the conflict. The government, desiring to quash leaders of the rebellion, hunted down Anacleto. He was jailed, tortured, and shot. His final words to his executioners were, "I die, but God does not! *¡Viva Cristo Rey!*"

The illustration's border design comes from the walls of the beautiful Shrine of Our Lady of Guadalupe in Guadalajara, Mexico, where Anacleto is laid to rest. The decorated skull is a symbol of the Day of the Dead, a holiday in Mexico to honor and remember those who have passed away. The skull is a reminder not of death as much as the beauty of the afterlife that all Christians hope to share with Christ the King.

As you color, consider how much you value your religious liberty. What would you be willing to do to protect it?

"[Christ the King's kingdom] rests on a higher power that wins over hearts: the love of God that he brought into the world with his sacrifice and the truth to which he bore witness. This is his sovereignty which no one can take from him and which no one should forget. . . . We ask Christ, to reign in our hearts, making them pure, docile, filled with hope and courageous in humility."

— Pope Benedict XVI, Homily in León, Mexico

Detachment and St. Ignatius of Loyola

As a young man, Ignatius (1491–1556) led a fascinating life, full of adventure and danger. He dreamed of marrying a beautiful woman and attaining honors and glory as an officer in the Spanish army. But his plans were interrupted when a cannonball hit his leg in battle. During the difficult recovery, Ignatius asked for a book on chivalry and romance. To his disappointment, the only book available was on the life of Christ and the saints. As he read, however, Ignatius experienced a spiritual awakening that enabled him to detach from his worldly dreams and to begin to seek holiness. Ignatius spent the following year living in a cave in the town of Manresa. He prayed, fasted, and attended Mass.

Throughout his life, Ignatius observed his emotional life closely as he strived for spiritual growth. Based on his personal experiences seeking to grow closer to God, Ignatius wrote his *Spiritual Exercises*, one of the most influential spiritual books ever written. At the beginning of the *Exercises*, Ignatius wrote of the importance of detachment—to make use of the things that bring one closer to God and to leave behind what does not. His writings continue to help the faithful discern when the devil is at work in one's life and when the Holy Spirit is active. Ignatius went on to found the Society of Jesus, also known as the Jesuits, a group of religious priests and brothers dedicated to working for the greater glory of God.

The illustration is reminiscent of a rose whose petals are first wound tightly together, then open up, and eventually fall to the ground. Although we might prefer to prolong the rose's more beautiful stages, the rose lives and dies according to God's design. The outward movement of the birds in the design signify a letting go or detachment. In order to follow God's will, one must be willing to leave behind what is very good and beautiful or at least to accept that it may not last forever. The quote in the illustration is from a Cursillo weekend, a method of spiritual renewal rooted in the Ignatian Spiritual Exercises. While not a direct quote from Ignatius, it reflects his teachings on detachment.

As you color, consider the things that stand in the way of your relationship with God. Do you need to let go of anything?

"Take, Lord, and receive all my liberty,
my memory, my understanding,
and my entire will—
all I have and possess.
You have given all to me.

To you, Lord, I return it.
All is yours; do with it what you will.
Give me only your love and your grace.
This is enough for me."

— St. Ignatius of Loyola, Suscipe Prayer

We must be willing to let go
of all that we hold most dear so
the evil one can have no hold on it.

Humility and St. Teresa of Calcutta

Mother Teresa (1910-1997) was born Agnes Gonxha Bojaxhiu in Skopje, the current capital of the Republic of Macedonia. At age eighteen, she decided to become a missionary religious sister with the Sisters of Loreto in Ireland. She took the name Sister Mary Teresa and soon departed for India where she made her first vows and began to teach in a convent school. One day as she rode a train to Darjeeling, she heard God ask her to serve the poorest of the poor. She received permission to leave the convent to follow this new call. She attended a course in basic medical training before setting out to live among the destitute in the slums of Calcutta. There she cared for the dying, the homeless, cripples, lepers, alcoholics, AIDS victims, orphans, the elderly, refugees—anyone who was suffering.

Mother Teresa embraced the people society discarded and strove to give them the help, love, and dignity that they deserved. She knew that she was just one person, able to do very little on her own. But she also knew that God could do great things through her. Mother Teresa's humility allowed her to see the face of Christ in the poor and to believe in God's great power. Inspired by Mother Teresa's courage and dedication, other young women began to help her and thus began the Missionaries of Charity. Today, the sisters, brothers, and priests of the Missionaries of Charity pray and serve the poor in hundreds of countries all over the world.

In the illustration one might recognize the hand of God reaching out to Adam from Michelangelo's *The Creation of Adam*. On the ceiling of the Sistine Chapel at St. Peter's Basilica in Rome, this breathtaking scene depicts the story of creation. The Book of Genesis recounts how God created humans in his image and likeness (1:27), giving *every* person an inherent dignity that cannot be lost. But humanity also shares the fate of Adam, fallen and vulnerable to evil, temptations, and darkness. True humility helps one to accept the reality of our sinfulness and to acknowledge God in any success.

As you color, contemplate how God created you to be in relationship with him. Reflect on God's infinite love for every person.

"Humility is the mother of all virtues; purity, charity, and obedience. It is in being humble that our love becomes real, devoted, and ardent. If you are humble nothing will touch you, neither praise nor disgrace, because you know what you are. If you are blamed, you will not be discouraged. If they call you a saint, you will not put yourself on a pedestal."

— St. Teresa of Calcutta

If you are humble,
nothing will touch you,
neither praise
nor disgrace,

because you
know what
you are.

— *St. Teresa of Calcutta*

Hospitality and St. Luke

Luke (1st century) was a physician believed to have come from Antioch in ancient Syria. A close confidant of St. Paul, Luke accompanied him on many of his missionary journeys. Luke's education and medical skills must have been useful in their travels. However, perhaps more notable was Luke's faithfulness to Paul in the face of great dangers. Shortly before his martyrdom in Rome, Paul wrote to Timothy: "Only Luke is with me" (2 Tim 4:11).

Luke was believed to be a Gentile, the only non-Jewish gospel writer. Perhaps for this reason his Gospel is the most welcoming and inclusive. Luke features the marginalized in his accounts, including the poor shepherds at the nativity, foreigners, tax collectors, beggars, lepers, and women. Luke also describes many meals where Jesus was in attendance. At one meal, Luke recounts how the Pharisees and scribes challenged Jesus because he welcomed sinners and tax collectors and sat with them. Jesus' response must have particularly resonated with Luke, the physician: "Those who are well have no need of a physician, but those who are sick; I have come to call not the righteous but sinners to repentance" (5:31–32).

The illustration is based on Caravaggio's 1601 painting, *The Supper at Emmaus*. Shortly after the resurrection, Luke relates in his Gospel that Jesus appeared to two disciples walking on the road to Emmaus (see 24:13–32). Though the two disciples did not recognize Jesus, they describe their hearts as "burning within" them as he spoke (24:32). When they arrived in Emmaus, the two disciples invited Jesus for supper. This scene depicts the moment when Jesus blesses and breaks the bread and the two disciples realize that he is the risen Christ. The innkeeper, standing at the left, looks on, uncomprehending.

As you color, reflect on how hospitable you are. Do you instantly recognize the inherent value of every person and welcome them with an open heart?

"Whoever welcomes this child in my name welcomes me, and whoever welcomes me welcomes the one who sent me; for the least among all of you is the greatest."

— Luke 9:48

Simplicity and St. Dominic

Dominic (1170–1221) was born to holy parents of Spanish nobility. He studied for ten years at university and was known for his intellectual discipline as well as his charity. He once sold his school books to give money to the poor. Dominic became a priest and was asked by his bishop to help combat the Albigensian heresy that was spreading fast in southern France. The Albigensians believed that all material creation was evil and so denied the incarnation of Jesus. Dominic combated the heresy simply by living a holy life and preaching. He had success because he lived a simple, virtuous life and practiced what he preached. He soon founded a religious order known as the Order of Preachers, later known as the Dominicans.

According to tradition, Dominic searched for the best way to powerfully communicate the faith to his uneducated Christian listeners. He prayed to Mary for help, and she counseled him to teach the stories of the Gospel by way of the Rosary. Simple, yet so powerful, the Rosary helped bring even greater success to Dominic's preaching. Centuries later, the Rosary is still a powerful devotion that helps people to understand the Gospel message.

The illustration is adapted from engravings in an early 20th-century Slavic book of Bible stories. The engravings are credited to the Nazarene School, which followed the 19th-century Germanic artistic movement known as Nazarene. Images include the Nativity (Lk 2:1–20), the Baptism of Jesus (Mt 3:13–17), the Crucifixion (Jn 19:17–30), and the Resurrection (Mt 28:1–10). The prayer at the center is the first stanza of *The Universal Prayer* attributed to Pope Clement XI (1649–1721). While not a part of the Rosary, this prayer expresses its purpose.

As you color and contemplate each of the scenes, consider the motivations behind Jesus' words and actions.

"I offer you, Lord, my thoughts to be fixed on you, my words to have you for their theme, my actions to reflect my love for you, my sufferings to be endured for your greater glory. I want to do what you ask of me in the way you ask, for as long as you ask, because you ask it. Lord, enlighten my understanding, strengthen my will, purify my heart, and make me holy."

— From *The Universal Prayer* attributed to Pope Clement XI

Lord, I believe in you; increase my faith. I trust in you; strengthen my trust. I love you; let me love you more and more.

— Pope Clement XI

Discernment and St. Peter

A simple Galilean fisherman, Simon Peter (1st century) must have been surprised when Jesus said to him, "Follow me" (Mt 4:19). A flawed, passionate man with a tendency to speak and act rashly, Peter was not the first person one might expect Jesus to call to be his disciple. Yet, Jesus not only called Peter, he entrusted him with great responsibility, declaring, "You are Peter, and on this rock I will build my church" (Mt 16:18). Even after Peter denied him three times, Jesus forgave him and continued to entrust him with the care of the early Christians (see Jn 21:15–19). Jesus knew that, with his grace, Peter would be able to lead the Church.

According to tradition, Peter fled Rome during the Christian persecution by the Emperor Nero around the year 67. On the road, Peter met the risen Christ. Seeing that Jesus was walking toward Rome, he asked him, *"Domine, quo vadis?"* or "Lord, where are you going?" Jesus replied, "I am going to Rome to be crucified again." Despite the danger, Peter turned back to Rome where he would be brutally martyred by upside-down crucifixion.

The illustration is based on the labyrinths built into the floors of many Gothic cathedrals in the medieval period. Labyrinths are not mazes, but winding paths that lead from the entrance to the center. They provide an opportunity for the faithful to take a simple "pilgrimage" of prayer. Walking a labyrinth allows one to get lost in contemplation while considering life's long, winding journey toward God. The four round alcoves in the design might represent places of rest or any distractions and concerns that might prevent one from moving forward in faith.

As you color, contemplate your life's path. Where are you going? What is your current direction and end goal? What are your aspirations, hurdles, and needs?

"My Lord God, I have no idea where I am going. I do not see the road ahead of me. I cannot know for certain where it will end. Nor do I really know myself, and the fact that I think I am following your will does not mean that I am actually doing so. But I believe that the desire to please you does in fact please you. And I hope I have that desire in all that I am doing. I hope that I will never do anything apart from that desire. And I know that if I do this, you will lead me by the right road, though I may know nothing about it. Therefore I will trust you always though I may seem to be lost and in the shadow of death. I will not fear, for you are ever with me, and you will never leave me to face my perils alone."

— THOMAS MERTON, *THOUGHTS IN SOLITUDE*

Zeal and St. Thérèse of Lisieux

Thérèse (1873–1897), also known as "The Little Flower," was born in the small town of Alençon, France. She was blessed with two loving and holy parents, Louis and Zelie Martin, who would also eventually be canonized as saints. When Thérèse was only four years old, one of the greatest sorrows of her life occurred: her mother died. Thérèse was already a frail, emotional child, but after her mother's death she grew even more sensitive and her health worsened. At age nine, Thérèse fell deathly ill but recovered miraculously after she had a vision of the Blessed Mother smiling upon her.

Despite ill health, Thérèse had very ambitious hopes to become a great martyr, a soldier of the faith, and a missionary to faraway lands. At the young age of fifteen, she found adventure in an unexpected way by following God's call to join the Carmelites of Lisieux. While Thérèse could not live out her adventurous dreams in the cloister, she continued to fight valiantly in the kingdom of God. She lived what she called the "Little Way," a simple commitment to acts of love, prayer, and sacrifice. Her daily efforts were like beautiful little flowers offered to the Lord. Thérèse was confident that her small actions would shine God's light and love on the world and participate in his victory over darkness. Near the end of her short life, in obedience to her superior, Thérèse wrote her autobiography, *The Story of a Soul*. She never imagined the impact her writings would have, but they have traveled all over the world and inspired millions. St. John Paul II recognized Thérèse as a Doctor of the Church.

The quote in the illustration is attributed to St. Joan of Arc in Thérèse's writings. She greatly admired Joan of Arc, the young, French peasant girl who centuries earlier had obeyed God's call to lead the French army into battle against England. Joan and Thérèse both had hearts on fire with love and were willing to give their lives for God. Thérèse once wrote in a prayer to Jesus: "I know the warfare in which I am to engage; it is not on the open field I shall fight. . . . My sword is Love! With it—like Joan of Arc—I will . . . have you proclaimed King over the Kingdom of souls!" Joan of Arc and Thérèse now share the title "Patroness of France."

As you color, consider how Thérèse lived her zeal for the faith in surprising ways. Ask God how you are called to grow in your passion for the faith.

"O my God! I offer you all my actions of this day for the intentions and for the glory of the Sacred Heart of Jesus. I desire to sanctify every beat of my heart, my every thought, my simplest works, by uniting them to its infinite merits; and I wish to make reparation for my sins by casting them into the furnace of its Merciful Love.

"O my God! I ask of you for myself and for those whom I hold dear, the grace to fulfill perfectly your Holy Will, to accept for love of you the joys and sorrows of this passing life, so that we may one day be united together in heaven for all eternity. Amen."

— St. Thérèse of Lisieux, A Morning Prayer

WE MUST DO
BATTLE BEFORE
GOD GIVES THE
VICTORY.

— ST. JOAN OF ARC

Reverence and St. Helena

Helena (c. 250–c. 330) was born to a simple, working-class family but later met and fell in love with the future Roman Emperor, Constantius. They had a son, Constantine, who would eventually rule the entire Roman Empire. The first Roman Emperor to convert to Christianity, Constantine became a Christian after he had a vision at the historic Battle of Milvian Bridge. Constantine's conversion was momentous, marking the beginning of tolerance for Christianity in the Roman Empire. His conversion also influenced Helena to take the Gospel to heart and to treasure it reverently as a pearl of great price (see Mt 13:45).

Constantine appointed his mother, Helena, to the royal court and allowed her to use the imperial treasury to locate holy relics and build churches. Helena traveled to the Holy Land and helped to reestablish many holy sites. She is perhaps most well-known for discovering the True Cross. To commemorate the site of the Cross' discovery, she had the Church of the Holy Sepulchre built in Jerusalem. Devoted not only to building churches, Helena also showed great generosity to the poor, soldiers, and others in need.

The illustration is drawn from a small section of the original mosaic floor in the Church of the Nativity in Bethlehem. British excavators discovered the floor in surprisingly good condition in the 1930s. Helena ordered the church built in the year 333 over the cave where Jesus was born.

As you color, consider the reverence of the artisans who worked on the mosaic floor in honor of the Lord. In what ways can you show more care and patience for love of God?

O give thanks to the LORD, call on his name,
 make known his deeds among the peoples.
Sing to him, sing praises to him,
 tell of all his wonderful works.
Glory in his holy name;
 let the hearts of those who seek the LORD rejoice.
Seek the LORD and his strength,
 seek his presence continually.
Remember the wonderful works he has done,
 his miracles, and the judgments he uttered,

O offspring of his servant Israel,
 children of Jacob, his chosen ones.
He is the LORD our God;
 his judgments are in all the earth.
Remember his covenant forever,
 the word that he commanded, for a thousand
  generations. . . .
O give thanks to the LORD, for he is good;
 for his steadfast love endures forever.

— KING DAVID'S PSALM OF THANKSGIVING,
1 CHRONICLES 16:8–15, 34

Loyalty and the Angels

The Bible refers to the existence of angels hundreds of times. The word "angel" comes from the Hebrew for "one sent" or messenger. At the foundation of the world, the angels were created to serve faithfully and eternally as helpers, protectors, messengers, and attendants before God. Though some angels rebelled and were cast out of heaven, the heavenly angels remain loyal servants of God. Angels generally appear in Scripture as God's messengers to humanity. The Angel Gabriel, for example, appeared to Mary to make the most important angelic announcement in salvation history—the birth of the Son of God (see Lk 1:26). All of the angels are saints because they are holy. Three angels in particular have traditionally been called "saint": Michael, Gabriel, and Raphael.

The saints also tell us a lot about the angels. St. John Chrysostom taught that during the Mass "angels stand by the priest; and the whole sanctuary, and the space round about the altar, is filled with [them]." St. Jerome wrote of the guardian angels, saying, "The dignity of the soul is so great that each person has an angel commissioned to guard him from birth." And St. Francis de Sales encouraged, "Make yourself familiar with the angels and behold them frequently in spirit. For, without being seen, they are present with you."

The illustration is drawn from a Victorian, hand-painted, stained glass window created by Heaton, Butler, and Bayne of London. These angels adore the newborn Christ. As has been the tradition since the 4th century, the angels are depicted with wings to signify that they are higher beings from heaven. Their wings are made of peacock feathers, a symbol of immortality.

As you color, think about times when your angel may have guided or protected you. Do you try to be aware of your guardian angel? Consider building a deeper friendship with your angel.

Angel of God, my guardian dear, to whom God's love commits me here,
ever this day be at my side, to light and guard, to rule and guide.
Amen.

— Prayer to the Guardian Angel, c. 11th century

About the Author/Illustrator

CINDI DUFT is a professional artist who has been commissioned to create more than fifty murals or paintings in Catholic churches and schools across her beautiful home state of Idaho. She is a cradle Catholic who attended twelve years of Catholic school before attaining degrees in art and business. She has ministered as a catechist for almost two decades in high school youth ministry, young adult ministry, and college ministry. Many of her paintings and murals can be seen at www.cindiduft.com.